GUM GIRL

★★ IN ★★

COUNTDOWN TO DESTRUCTION!

ANDI WATSON

WALKER

**To Ilya, Woodrow and Paul Gravett,
who were there at the start**

This is a work of fiction. Names, characters, places and incidents
are either the product of the author's imagination or, if real, used fictitiously.

First published 2013 by Walker Books Ltd

87 Vauxhall Walk, London SE11 5HJ

2 4 6 8 10 9 7 5 3 1

Text & Illustrations © 2013 Andi Watson

The right of Andi Watson to be identified as author of this work has been asserted by him
in accordance with the Copyright, Designs and Patents Act 1988

This book has been typeset in Block T

Printed and bound in Malaysia

British Library Cataloguing in Publication Data: a catalogue record for this
book is available from the British Library

ISBN 978-1-4063-2941-4

www.walker.co.uk   www.gumgirl.co.uk

6

Well, the Temporal Extractor Unit allows me to break up the time line into small parcels and store them in here.

Basically, you're stealing time from school kids. Not quite what Einstein had in mind for his Quantum Theory.

School children have more time to spare than anyone.

I have stolen nothing. I'm merely redistributing wasted time and putting it into the service of Science.

If they're not running around mindlessly yelling, they're wasting time on the Internet, staring out of the window daydreaming, fidgeting or faffing with their mobile phones.

That explains why breaktime and lunch went by so quickly – the minutes have been nicked!

That's where you keep all the time you've collected, you say?

Mr Higgins!
WAH.
Waaaaaah.
Stick around, baby.
Can't ... hold ... on...
How am I supposed to stop a Time Sink?
Of course!

35

38

41

42

49

51

55

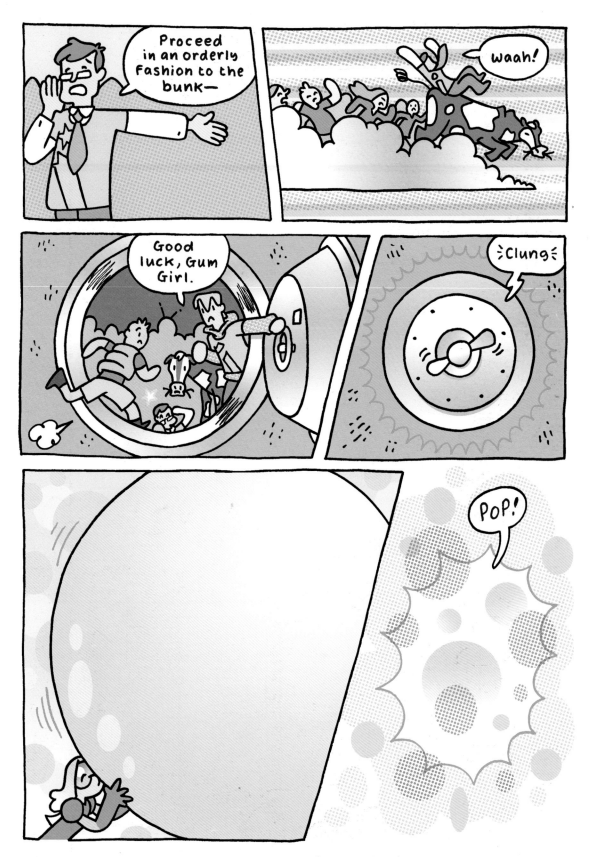